Our house

Story written by Gill Munton
Illustrated by Tim Archbold

Speed Sounds

Consonants   *Ask children to say the sounds.*

f	l	m	n	r	s	v	z	sh	th	ng
ff	ll	mm	nn	rr	ss	ve	zz			nk
ph	(le)	mb	(kn)	wr	(se)		se			
					(ce)		s			

b	c	d	g	h	j	p	qu	t	w	x	y	ch
bb	kk	dd	gg		j	pp		tt	wh			tch
	ck		(gu)		ge							

Each box contains one sound but sometimes more than one grapheme.
*Focus graphemes for this story are **circled**.*

Vowels *Ask children to say the sounds in and out of order.*

a	e ea	i	o	u	ay	ee y e	igh i	ow o
at	hen	in	on	up	day	see	high	blow

oo	oo	ar	or oor ore	air	ir	**ou**	oy oi
zoo	look	car	for	fair	whirl	shout	boy

5

Story Green Words

Carl   shout   couch   flour   pound   snout   proud   our   doubt*   guess*

Ask the children to say the syllables and then read the whole word.

Boun|der   boun|cy   grou|chy   sham|poo   knock|out   grey|hound*

Ask children to read the root first and then the whole word with the suffix.

pounce → pounced   devour → devoured   wash → washing*

hour → hours*

* Challenge Words

6

Vocabulary Check

Discuss the meaning (as used in the story) after the children have read each word.

	definition:	**sentence:**
doubt	don't think so	I doubt if you'd bother to stop next to it.
pound	hurt	Carl plays his CDs so loud my head starts to pound.
grouchy	grumpy	Mum can get a bit grouchy.
couch	sofa	We have our dinner on the couch.
pounced	jumped	He pounced on it …
devoured	ate really quickly	… and devoured it at top speed.
snout	dog's nose	Bounder stuck his snout into my hand.
knockout	really good	He's a knockout at football.

Red Words

Ask children to practise reading the words across the rows, down the columns and in and out of order clearly and quickly.

anyone	over	who	all
one	watch	does	they
school	you	to	were
was	said	wasn't	want
water	some	their	there

Our house

Our house isn't much to look at.

I doubt if you'd bother to stop next to it

if you went along Mount Street (that's our street).

Not that anyone much goes along Mount Street.

(It's that kind of street.)

Our house is sort of pink, with a red door and a little

garden all round it. I can't begin to count the weeds in that garden.

And Bounder (Grandad's greyhound) is always digging

up the ground, looking for his bouncy ball.

We've got three bedrooms – one for Mum, one
for Grandad (and Bounder) and one for me and Carl.
Carl plays his CDs for hours, so loud that – ouch!
– my head starts to pound.

Then Mum shouts up the stairs
and says "Stop that!".
(She can get a bit grouchy, our Mum.)

Most days we have our dinner on the couch, watching TV.
Last week, Bounder found a bit of
egg sandwich next to Grandad's chair.

He pounced on it and
devoured it at top speed.

Yuck.

We've just got one small bathroom.

So when Bounder's having his bath,

you can forget about going to the loo

or washing your hands

for about ten hours.

Grandad gets shampoo and

dog hairs all over the floor –

and guess who gets to mop it up!

I'm in bed as I'm telling you all this.
I was just thinking – it doesn't sound much,
our house. But it's not that bad.
Tonight, Mum sent me to the corner shop
to get some flour and I got a pound,
for sweets. They were so good, I stuffed about
six into my mouth.

When I got back, Bounder stuck his snout into my hand and
started to lick my arm. They're fantastic dogs, greyhounds, and so fast!
Bounder can run at about 60 km an hour.

Then Carl and I went out to Southways Park to have a kickabout in the playground. He's a knockout at football, our Carl.
He plays for our school. I guess I'm proud of him.

And when I went to bed,
Grandad chatted to me as
I brushed my teeth.

Then he said, was I too old for a story.

I said no, I wasn't.

Our house is ...

... too small

... full of shouting

... a bit of a mess (well, some days).

But it's never boring.

Our house is – well, it's all right.

Questions to talk about

Ask children to TTYP each question using 'Fastest finger' (FF) or 'Have a think' (HaT).

p.9 (HaT)   How do we know the garden isn't pretty?

(HaT)   How do we know it's a quiet street?

p.10 (FF)   Why does his head begin to pound?

p.11 (FF)   What do they do while they eat their dinner?

p.12 (HaT)   Why can't anyone wash their hands when Bounder has a bath?

p.13 (FF)   What did he buy when he went to the shops?

p.14 (FF)   Why is he proud of Carl?

(HaT)   What does he get Grandad to do?

p.15 (FF)   What does he like about his house?

Questions to read and answer

(Children complete without your help.)

1. What does the house look like? The house has …

2. Why is Mum grouchy? She is grouchy because …

3. What happens when Bounder has a bath? When Bounder has a bath …

4. What is Carl good at? Carl is good at …

5. Why is your house a good house? It is good because …

Speedy Green Words

Ask children to practise reading the words across the rows, down the columns and in and out of order clearly and quickly.

garden	ground	loud	stairs
found	sound	always	tonight
house	look	have	next
along	street	little	looking
having	thinking	story	right